The Little Book of Pigs and Piglets

Porcine poetry, legends and history
for all porcinophiles

Edited by
Susan Fortunato and
Giema Tsakuginow

MICHAEL O'MARA BOOKS LIMITED

We gratefully acknowledge the following artists and representatives for letting us use their work: Mike Wepplo, Gay Bumgarner, Scott Anderson, Debra E. Arnold, Scott Pollack, William Akunevicz, Jr., Jerry Howard, Cynthia Watts Clarke, Bryant Haynes, Lisa Palombo, The Den of Antiquities, Stockworks, Eileen Moss Representative, Positive Images, The Image Bank and Artworks.

HOG WILD ☺

First Published in Great Britain in 1995 by Michael O' Mara Books Ltd, 9 Lion Yard, Tremadoc Road, London SW4 7NQ

Copyright © 1992 by Longmeadow Press

First Published in the United States of America by Longmeadow Press

A CIP catalogue record of this book is available from the British Library.

Text design: Barbara Cohen Aronica

ISBN: 1-85479-646-1
Printed in Singapore
1 3 5 7 9 10 8 6 4 2

To Chris & Graham

"The time has come," the Walrus said,
    "To talk of many things:
Of shoes—of ships—and sealing wax
    of cabbages—and kings—
And why the sea is boiling hot—
    And whether pigs have wings."

> —*Lewis Carroll,*
> *Through the Looking Glass,*
> *1871*

■ 9 ■

Pro-Pigganda

Pigs Are Not Stupid

It is well documented, although still not well received, that
a pig's intelligence is far more comparable to that of a
dolphin than of a horse or a cow.

Pigs Are Not Dirty

The image of the pig wallowing in mud has probably done
more to hold the pig back from becoming a premiere
household pet than any other misconception. But wallowing
serves an important purpose. It protects the skin from sun
and insects. A pig's skin is very delicate, much like our own,
and pigs have very few sweat glands, so it is vital that they
keep themselves protected and cool in the hot sun.

Pigs Are Not Greedy

When trained, a pig is just a loyal and well mannered as a cocker spaniel. The writer Milan Kundera wrote in his novel *The Unbearable Lightness of Being* about a pig, Mefisto, and his relationship with a man, Tomas.

The collective farm chairman became a truly close friend. He had a wife, four children, and a pig he raised like a dog. The pig's name was Mefisto, and he was the pride and the main attraction of the village. He would answer his master's call and was always clean and pink; he paraded about on his hoofs like a heavy-thighed woman in high heels.

Some, like the Roman poet Horace, were early advocates of the pig's virtues. In fact, he was so won over by the virtues of the pig that he described himself as "a shining pig from the herd of Epicurus."

There exists perhaps in all creation no animal which has less justice and more injustice shown him than the pig.

—*Sir Francis Bond Head*

Myth Piggies

The pig always inspires passion. An unlikely hero, it
lacks the strength of the ox and the grace of the horse,
and he is certainly too cute and pink to present a
convincing threat. Yet the pig's place in mythology and
legend is almost universal. Maybe it is the duality of
pigs that makes them so appealing to the collective
imagination.

The paradise of my fancy is one where pigs have wings.

—*G.K. Chesterton*

Ancient Greek Pigs

In ancient Greece the sow symbolized fertility and was an important part of religious ceremonies and tradition. Demeter, the goddess of corn, was often represented as a sow. Even the Eleusinian mysteries, which were celebrated by both the Greeks and the Romans, and are still shrouded in secrecy, had the sow playing a major role. The Romans also identified the pig with the goddess Maia, calling the pig *maialis*, or the one dear to the heart of Maia.

The Swine Who Would Be Swine

Perhaps the most famous Greek legend of the pig is in the *Odyssey*. Ulysses had just witnessed all but one of his ships destroyed by the Laestrygones when his ship came to the island of Aiaie and he sent a party of his men to explore. He didn't realize that the island was run by a beautiful witch named Circe who turned all men who dared come onto her island into beasts. When she saw Ulysses's men, she turned them into swine, but kept their human minds so they would be aware of this state.

One of Ulysses's men managed to escape and tell him the fate of his companions. Ulysses started out alone for Circe's house, but on his way he encountered Hermes. Hermes gave Ulysses an herb that would stop Circe's magic, so that later, when Circe used her magic and Ulysses was able to resist, Circe fell in love with him and agreed to release all of his men.

Some versions of the story, however, have Ulysses's men convincing him not to restore them to men at all, but to let them remain pigs. This is the version we pig lovers like to hear.

Pigs see the wind.

—*Wiltshire saying*

You Lucky Pig

Legend has it that Buddha, upon leaving Earth, summoned all the animals to him. The pig was the last of twelve to appear. Persons born in a Year of the Pig can consider themselves to have the qualities of a pig—patience and a balanced disposition.

According to the Chinese horoscope, 1995 was a Year of the Pig.

Watch Out for the P—I—G

Some cultures won't even say the **P** word. The Scotch called them "short-legged ones," "the grunting animal," or the "grunters." In the Talmud the pig is referred to as *davaraher*, the Hebrew phrase for "another thing," and observant Jews are not supposed to mention the pig. To this day, some fishermen in Nova Scotia are so frightened of this curse that they would bring their boat into dock if anyone on board mentioned a pig.

Good Luck to you
on St Patrick's Day

Good Fortune
on St Patrick's Day.

Pig Pals

To market, to market, to buy a fat pig,
Home again, home again, jiggety-pig.

We have been cheering on the pig since we were old
enough to turn the pages of The Three Little Pigs, so
it should come as no surprise that some of the most
influential political, spiritual, and literary figures were
also porcinophiles. Reading about the pig's role in
history, how can you help but wonder what the dog's
résumé would look like in comparison?

Hollywood Hogs

Porky Pig
Piggly Wiggly
Miss Piggy

A person who has an affection for pigs is called a porcinophile.

The Most Expensive Pig

Glacier, a Duroc boar was sold to Wilbert and Myron Meinhart
of Hudson, Iowa for $42,500 February 24, 1979.

Famous Friends of Pigs

Some of the more famous porcinophiles:

James Dean
Thomas à Becket
James Taylor
Sir Walter Scott
Michael Korda

The Pig-Saint Connection

St. Anthony

The most important pig lover of all was St. Anthony, the first Christian monk. As a young man, St. Anthony began to practise an acetic life. During his year of solitary prayer and meditation, he was often tested by Satan, who once came to him in the form of a grunting, thrashing pig. St. Anthony did not slay the pig, who tore at him with his horns and teeth. Instead, he prevailed with his calm faith. Then a wondrous light enveloped him, driving the demon away, leaving him in the light company of a humble, innocent pig.

In years to come, European monks would select certain pigs to be spared from slaughter. They would tie bells around the pig's neck and go out seeking alms with the pigs at their side. The pigs became known as "tantony" pigs in honour of St. Anthony, the patron saint of pigs.

Several other saints have been aided in their holy ascents by our portly friends. Here is a list of how pigs have assisted them:

Saint	Pig Connection
St. Brannoc	Sow and piglet led him to future church site
St. Kentigern	Pig tilled the land where his church was built
St. Malo	The Saint healed pig and got land for his church from the pig's grateful owner
St. Oswald	Pig moved church construction to site where Saint died

This little pig went to market

This little piggy went to
   market;
This little pig stayed home;
This little pig had roast beef;
This little pig had none;
And this little pig cried, Wee,
   wee, wee!
All the way home.

Askel Gedee of Denmark was the proud owner of the largest litter of piglets in the world: 34, born June 25–26, 1961.

The Hail Piggy Play

During the English Civil War the royalist army was
laying siege to the city of Gloucester. The city was near
collapse until, in a last desperate gambit, the last
remaining pig was sent squealing along the perimeter of
the city. The king, imagining a multitude of pigs, and
ample stores for the city to continue holding out,
withdrew his army.

Sébastien Le Prestre, Comte de Vauban (1633–1707), Piggy Banker

How many pigs would a pregnant sow parent, grandparent, and great-grandparent in a ten–year period? This question and many more were answered by this French nobleman and military engineer who calculated that a pregnant sow and her children would increase the pig population by 6,434,338 in a mere decade. This led Vauban to conclude that if you could buy one animal with which to make your fortune, it should be a pig.

The gestation period for a pig is three months,
three weeks and three days.

Pigpourri

Truffles

In a world of processed cheese and indoor grills, its good to remember that some of the best things in life are inconvenient. The pig, in his relentless pursuit of his favourite fungi, reminds us of this as often as he can.

These mushrooms grow at the base of certain oak trees and can be harvested between November and March. The pig has traditionally been used to find elusive truffles. He is so fond of them and his sense of smell so developed that he can root out their scent. Unfortunately for their human companions, the pigs, having found their prize, are loath to surrender their delicacies, even for the going rate of about £200 a pound.

The most prized truffles come from the Perigord region of France. They are a deep black, in comparison with Italian "white" truffle, which is really a dark brown or beige.

"P Stands for Pig"

P stands for Pig, as I remarked before,
A second cousin to the Huge Wild Boar
But pigs are civilised, while Huge Wild Boars
Live savagely, at random, out of doors,
And in their coarse contempt of dainty foods,
Subsist on truffles, which they find in woods.
Not so the cultivated Pig who feels
The need of several courses at his meals,
But wrongly thinks it does not matter whether
He takes them one by one or all together.
Hence, Pigs devour, from lack of self respect,
what Epicures would certainly reject.

MORAL:
Learn from the Pig to take whatever Fate
Or Elder Persons heap upon your plate.

Hilaire Belloc, A Bad Child's Book of Beasts, 1940

Pig–tionary

Shoat—A young pig

Pig—A small domestic animal

Hog—A pig that weighs over 120 pounds

Boar—An adult male

Sow—An adult female

Swine—Pigs, hogs, boars, and sows.

Mud Baths in Bath

In 863 B.C. the city of Bath was founded on the site where Baldred was cured of leprosy. Baldred's father, the king of the Britons, had sent him to study in Greece, but while there he was struck with leprosy. He returned to England, but was only fit to be a swineherd because of his disease. He noticed that the pigs wallowed in the mud, and their skin problems seemed to be minimized.
The mud bath was born, and Baldred's leprosy was cured.

The sow came in with the saddle
The little pig rocked the cradle,
The dish jumped up on the table
To see the pot swallow the ladle.

There was an old man of Messina
Whose daughter was named Opsibeena;
She wore a small wig,
and rode out on a pig,
To the perfect delight of Messina.

Edward Lear, More Nonsense, 1872

Pigs may whistle,
but they ha'e an
ill mouth for't.

—*Scottish proverb*

PALOMBO

In the Hindu religion, the boar represents the third incarnation of Vishnu. In a thousand-year battle to save the world from evil, the boar, Varaha, dived down to the bottom of the ocean and saved the earth. In Indian art, he is shown balancing the world on his tusks.

Piggy Poet

W.B. Yeats, perhaps the greatest modern poet, was also the father of pig poetry publishing poems such as the "Valley of the Black Pig" and "Swine of the Gods."

How you say pig?

Language	Word for Pig
French	cochon
German	schwein
Italian	maiale
Spanish	puerco
Japanese	buta
Danish	gris
Turkish	domuz
Romanian	porc
Portugese	leito
Serbo-croatian	syinja

In Ireland it was considered good luck to have a pig driven into your house on the first of May, but bad luck the rest of the year.

The Empress of Blandings

There was only one thing to be done, if he hoped to recover calm
of spirit. He straightened his pince-nez, and went off to the
piggeries to have a look at Empress of Blandings.

The Empress lived in a bijou residence not far from the kitchen
garden, and when Lord Emsworth arrived at her boudoir she was
engaged, as pretty nearly always when you dropped in on her, in
hoisting into her vast interior those fifty-seven thousand and eight
calories on which Whiffle insists. Monica Simmons, the pig girl,
had done her well in the way of barley meal, maize meal, linseed
meal, potatoes, and separated buttermilk, and she was digging in
and getting hers in a manner calculated to inspire the brightest
confidence in the bosoms of her friends and admirers.

P. G. Wodehouse - Pigs Have Wings

My Silly Sandwich

by Liza Charlesworth

ISBN: 978-1-338-29798-0

Illustrated by Tammie Lyon
Copyright © 2018 by Liza Charlesworth
First printing, June 2018.

■SCHOLASTIC

Hi! I am Sid.
I like to make silly sandwiches.

This is my dog, Spot.
He likes to watch.

You are in luck!
I will make a silly sandwich
right now.

I put on lots of ham.

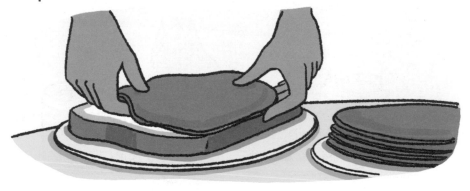

I put on lots of cheese.

I put on lots of pickles.

I put on lots of noodles.

I put on lots of jelly beans.

I put on lots of ketchup.

All done!
I told you my sandwich was silly.
Now, I will get some milk
to go with it.

I am back.
Hey!
Where did my sandwich go?

Did my mom eat it?
"No, your sandwiches
are too silly," she says.

Did my dad eat it?
"No, your sandwiches
are too silly," he says.

Did my sister eat it?
"No, your sandwiches
are too silly," she says.

Hey!
Who ate my sandwich?
Wait.
I see some crumbs.

I follow them.
Crumb, crumb, crumb.

Crumb, crumb, crumb.

Hey!
Spot ate my sandwich.
Now, that is too silly!